P9-DGZ-885

You'll Always Be

Written by Callie Jade Fryt
Illustrated by Rachel Batislaong

You may not remember me,
but mommy will tell you I was as sweet as can be.
I was your sibling and your best friend.
I'm sure you had a unique nickname for me.

Although I'm not physically by your side,
I know we would be as cool
as butterflies.

One day, we will meet again and
do such fun things together.

We will laugh, play, and do all the things that best friends do.

We will feed the cranes,
build sand castles,
play with dragonflies, and even
swim against the cool waves at the beach.

Mommy and daddy will be so excited
when that day comes.

Until then, do not be sad that I am gone.
I will always be with you and you will always be with me.

We will forever be siblings and our love will continue to grow.

Keep your faith strong, until we meet again.
I love you, forever, my sibling you'll always be.

Callie Fryt was inspired to write a children's book after the passing of her 4 year old son, Kaiden. Callie had a hard time finding a book that would explain the situation to her 2 year old daughter, Madeline. Callie loves spending time with family, cooking, and cleaning. She, in fact, opened up a cleaning business in the memory of her son. Callie also enjoys taking trips to Florida with her mother, which happened to be Kaiden's favorite place. Callie has worked in the healthcare field the last six years and will continue to do that.

This children's book is dedicated to the families suffering the loss of a child.
Loss between siblings is heartbreaking for everyone involved.
It is my hope that this will provide some comfort to those in need by keeping their loved ones memory alive.

For Kaiden Glaspie

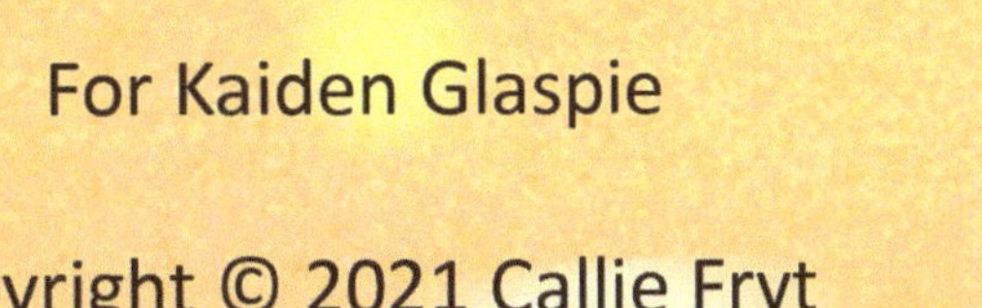

Copyright © 2021 Callie Fryt
Art Copyright © 2021 Rachel Batislaong
All Rights Reserved
ISBN: 978-0-578-84849-5
For more information about this book please contact:
Calliefryt@yahoo.com